14.99

14.99

- Dylan George • Abby Nicol • Matt Ray
- Caitlen James • Danielle Dean • Cole Henningsen
- Ryan Egan • Reese Icenogle • Reilly L.

Kevin Ness • Cayden Gorman • Kyra Mowry

Samantha Bryson • Nicole chan • Nate Sage

- Gianna Biggerstaff • Evan Smith

• Valerie Ulsh • Jade Martin

- camden Drown

Happy Reading from your 4th grade authors!

Respect Responsibility Rigor

Cover illustration by Cole Henningsen

The Three R's
Make The World Go Around

Written and illustrated by Mrs. Robinson's fourth grade class
at Coyote Ridge Elementary School in Broomfield, Colorado

On The Write Path Publishing
5023 W 120th Ave. #228
Broomfield, CO 80020
(303) 465-2056
OnTheWritePath1@aol.com

Coyote Ridge Elementary School
13770 Broadlands Drive
Broomfield CO 80023
720-972-5780

Meet the Authors

Bottom Row, left to right: Abbey Nicol, Dylan George, Jade Martin, Cayden Gorman
2nd Row, left to right: Reese Icenogle, Mrs. Robinson, Caitlen James, Nathan Sage, Gianna Biggerstaff, Kevin Ness, Ryan Egan, Matthew Ray **3rd Row, left to right:** Kyra Mowry, Reilly Lavelle **4th Row, left to right:** Nicole Chan, Evan Smith **5th Row, left to right:** Camden Brown, Danielle Dean, Samantha Bryson, Valerie Ulsh, Cole Henningsen

This book is dedicated to all our friends at Coyote Ridge Elementary

Intro

What are the Three R's that make the world go around? Well, in our world, at Coyote Ridge Elementary, the three R's come directly from the student-generated, positively-stated, school-wide expectations.

Last year, a student suggested that we develop a school-wide motto of expected rules for all Coyote Ridge students. Thanks to this student's leadership, and from the input of students and staff at Coyote Ridge, we focused on responsibility, respect, and rigor. We coined the catchy slogan, CR3, which stands for Coyote Ridge Three top traits, for all to remember.

The students in my fourth grade classroom are constantly on the lookout for new ways to demonstrate these traits at home and at school. This book is filled with real life stories told from the students' personal experiences and is dedicated to their enthusiastic and tireless efforts to learn these traits.

I hope you enjoy reading these stories as much as I have!

Forever learning,
Mrs. Karen Robinson

respect

rigor

responsibility

respect

rigor

responsibility

respect

rigor

Respect

Thump! Boom! There she goes again! Always in a rush and never taking her time, my little sister continually falls or is bumping into something. It definitely takes a lot of patience to show my sister respect. I have to remind myself over and over how important it is to be kind to others and appreciate their differences as well as their similarities.

I show respect to my little sister by praising her and being proud of the special person she is. She has learning disabilities and sometimes has a hard time understanding and expressing herself. I tutor her and calmly work with her, often hugging her and letting her know how well she is doing. I read to her each night, and remind her that she's amazing, and I'm blessed to have her as my sister. She learns differently than I do, and sometimes it is hard to be compassionate with her. That's the time I know I need to compliment her and support her the most. There are times that I have to explain things ten times, and guess what? Yep, she still doesn't get it! I wonder if anyone ever gets this frustrated with me!

Being polite and respectful to people shows them that they are valuable. When we stop and realize that everyone is a unique individual, yet equally important, it is much easier to appreciate people for who they are.

By: Jade Martin

Respect

Have you ever made a special effort to show respect to an adult at school? Respect is being caring and considerate, like letting someone have something when you are done. It is also doing someone a favor. Respect is helping people, and being friendly to everyone.

I show respect at school by doing favors for Ms. Laurie, our school custodian. It is really helpful when I carry things for her, or hold the door open so she can easily walk through. Without Ms. Laurie's hard work, our school would not be the same. I realize that I should be courteous to everyone, making their jobs easier in any way I can.

I've learned that if you are respectful to everybody, they will show respect back to you. Respect shows strength of character, and it is appreciated by everyone.

By: Kevin Ness

respect responsibility rigor respect responsibility rigor

respect responsibility rigor respect responsibility rigor respect responsibility

rigor respect responsibility rigor respect responsibility

Respect

Crash! Pain can be a very valuable thing to help you learn respect! I got a face full of elbow from my little sister that helped me learn to show respect by giving people their own personal space. My accident taught me to treat others respectfully so that less pain comes my way!

Giving people respect is important in many ways. One way to show respect is to give people space. My sister and I were at a lacrosse game when we decided to go get a slushy. It was really crowded and everyone was pushing ahead to get in the concession stand line. My little sister rammed into me with her elbow and pow! My face was numb and I was in shock! She didn't mean to hurt me, but with all of the pushing, it was hard to move. That slushy sure tasted good and felt good against my swollen face!

My sister showed respect to me by saying she was sorry and helping me up off the cold floor. There are lots of terrific ways to show respect, but the most important way is treating others like you want to be treated. My slushy accident taught me a valuable lesson. So that goes to show you that you should give people personal space so that you don't have to buy an extra slushy for your headache!

By: Caitlen James

Respect

Playing a game can be fun, but don't lose your mind like I did! Respect means to hold someone or something in high regard, and not to be greedy when competing. When I play a game, I'm either a sore loser or an unbearable winner, but I don't do it on purpose! It's just a really bad habit I have. Doesn't everybody think it is hard to respect their competitors?

A few days ago, I was playing "Just Dance" with my oldest sister and my mom. I was winning the first few rounds, but then my luck changed, and I started losing. In my mind, two conversations were going on. One was telling me to block the television, and not to let Abby win. The other one was saying, "It's okay to lose, everyone does." I knew the second voice was right, but I love to win! I decided that I was going to block the TV, but then changed my mind and moved out of the way just in time. As much as I wanted to be the winner, I didn't want to lose the respect my mom and sister had for me by making the wrong decision. I mean, who would give up respect for a game?

Although I didn't win, I was happy that I didn't do something really foolish and lose my mother's and sister's respect. You may think that winning is everything, but hey! Would you seriously want to lose the respect someone has for you? It's been difficult, but I've learned that winning isn't everything, and I should always remember to respect my family members and friends. I wouldn't want to learn the hard way. Remember, respect is the best choice to make!

By: Danielle Dean

respect

rigor

responsibility

respect

rigor

responsibility

respect

rigor

Respect

"Nicole, I'm here!"

"Oh no, not now," I said to myself in a quiet voice. Immediately I ran upstairs, but unfortunately he heard my footsteps! In my mind, I was thinking about how my little cousin was going to distract me from getting my homework done. How could I show respect to the little pest and still manage to finish my homework?

My prediction was right! He quickly ran upstairs and found me. It took him no time to start bothering me. I asked him to stop it a hundred times, but he wouldn't listen. Then I asked myself, "Why did he have to come today when I have so much homework?"

He left my room and I thought it was for good, but he came back! I felt so frustrated and angry. Then, I told him about respect. I said, "If you don't show respect to people, then they won't show it to you."

Guess what happened next? My cousin stopped bugging me and I was able to finish my homework. If I had been more respectful of him in the first place, he would probably have tried to be respectful to me.

My little cousin is still learning about respect and I am too! After I talked to him, he never bothered me again. So, now my cousin is showing respect to everybody, even people he doesn't know.

By: Nicole Chan

Respect

Crash! There went my interest in showing respect. One night, I was disrespectful at dinner and I didn't get into trouble. No one seemed to notice or care that I was being rude. Made me wonder why I should go to the trouble of showing respect at all. That was until one very special day.

One Friday morning, my class and I went to a retirement home for seniors so we could get to know each other. Our teacher planned a monthly program to share different activities with our "grands," so they could spend time with kids and we could learn from them. Right away, I knew I had to show respect and be on my best behavior. When we got there, I greeted everybody and listened to what they had to say. Then we played games, but before I yelled out my answer, I asked my grand for his advice. Next, it was time for snacks, but I made sure that all of the seniors at my table were served first. At the end, we had to say our farewells, and I was very careful not to leave anyone out.

Wow! I have my interest for respect back! Now I can see why it is so important to show respect all of the time. And guess what? It feels good to be respectful of others and have them show respect to me too. From now on, I'm going to show respect everywhere, especially at the retirement home!

By: Cayden Gorman

Respect

Have you ever seen steam pour out of your mom's ears? Respect is something I really had to learn! You should always use your manners. Saying please and thank you is important, and I learned my lesson the hard way!

One evening, I didn't use my manners at dinner. I demanded that my food be ready too fast. My mom was standing there waiting for me to say please. She got madder and madder the longer she waited, until I thought she would explode!

Eventually, she asked, "Aren't you going to say something?" I just looked at her. "Please and thank you," she crossly said.

"I'm sorry," I whispered.

"It's okay," she sighed.

Now, I say please and thank you all the time. I even get complimented for being polite. I no longer have to be reminded to be respectful.

Respect is so important. A good way to show it is to use your manners. I will never forget that again!

By: Abbey Nicol

respect

rigor

responsibility

respect

rigor

responsibility

respect

rigor

Responsibility

Talk about a frustrating situation! Just when my friend arrived for a much antic-ipated sleepover and we were ready to have the pillow fight of all time, my mom said first I had to clean up my room. Where were super powers when I needed them? I was really in for it!

We started by cleaning up toys and DS cartridges. We organized games and models by theme, and put away books by genre. It took difficult categorizing and plenty of effort, but we eventually got everything spotless. Mom was amazed at the short amount of time it took, and gave us a "Great job!"

Responsibility means doing what you are supposed to do, even if no one is watching. If you show it in what you do, it can really pay off! Also, knowing you did a good deed makes you feel like a dog in a dog park; very happy.

Now, let the pillows fly, man!

By: Matthew Ray

respect responsibility rigor respect responsibility rigor

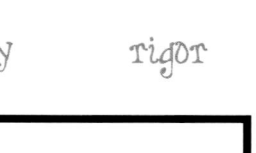

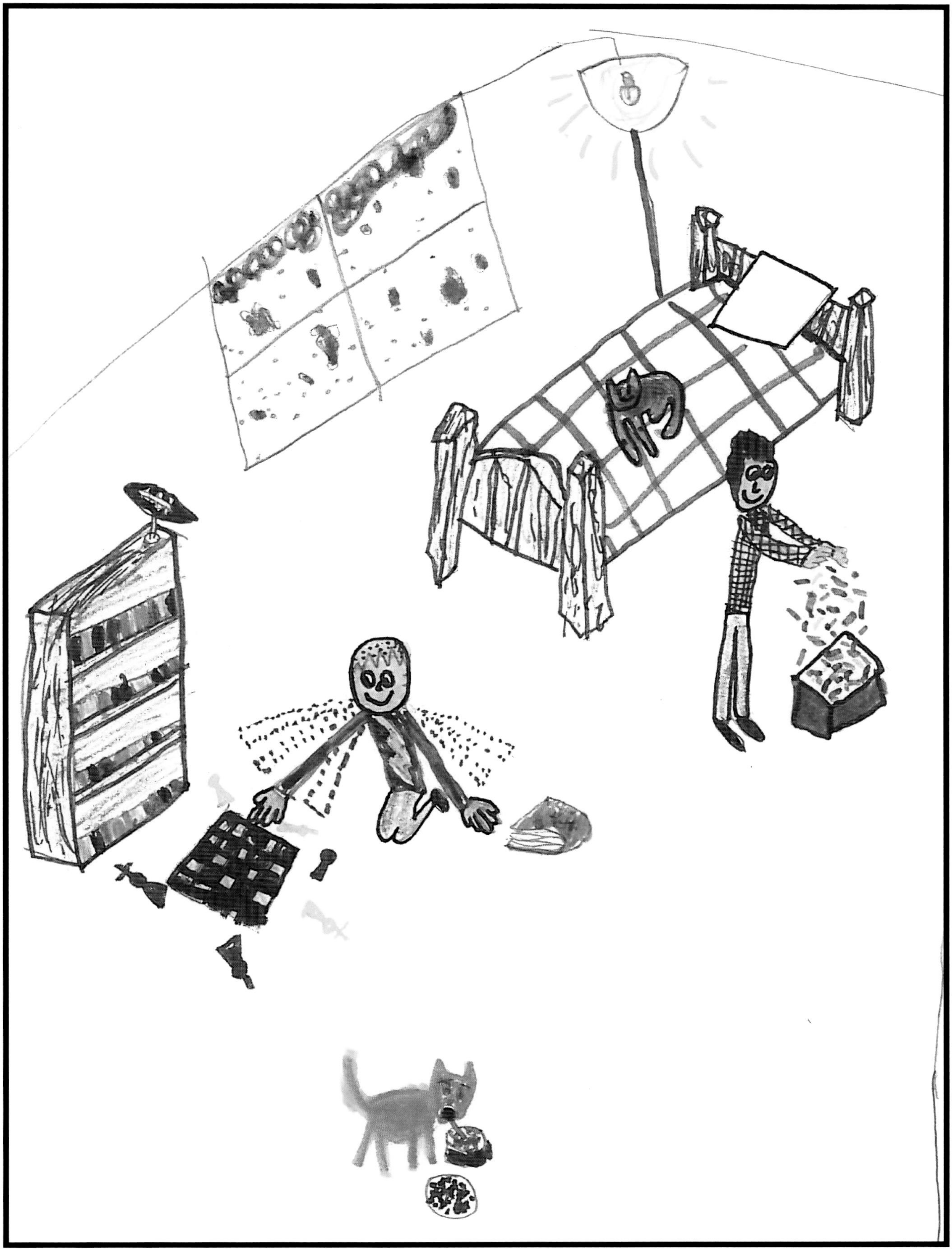

Responsibility

Living in a pigsty is not a lot of fun, especially when it's your room. Leaving trash and toys and junk all over your bedroom does not show responsibility. It's not fun picking it all up. Trust me, it's not.

One busy afternoon, I had just come home from school and my mom demanded that I pick up everything scattered all over my room. When I went upstairs, toys and pillows were popping out from under the bedroom door. When I pushed open the door, I couldn't find my bed anywhere! There were tall piles of junk sandwiched between stacks of dirty clothes, and there were all sorts of toys in every corner. I couldn't help but gasp as I looked around, and I didn't know where to start. It must have taken me at least three hours to pick it all up. Whew!

The worst part was I had to organize everything! Learning responsibility is a very long process, just like keeping your room clean. I learned the hard way how important it is to keep my bedroom and everything that belongs to me tidy and in order. That's how you show responsibility. You'll be much happier and so will your mom!

By: Nathan Sage

Responsibility

I thought I wouldn't get yelled at. I really believed it was okay to throw trash out of the car window, but it wasn't. Responsibility is taking care of things that are yours. You need to show responsibility so you don't get in trouble like I did. But, there's another reason why you don't want to be a litter bug!

I learned an important lesson about taking care of the Earth. We were driving to Minnesota to see my grandparents, and my brother was sitting next to me in the backseat. As soon as we saw Mom reaching into her purse, we knew what she was getting. Together, my brother and I started to yell, "Give us some gum, give us some gum!"

"Okay, okay," Mom said as she handed a piece to each of us. The gum was in our mouths as fast as lightning. After a couple of minutes, I didn't want to hold the wrapper anymore so I rolled down the window. I threw out the wrapper and watched it tumble over the rocky road of beautiful Minnesota.

My mom saw the whole thing happen and she exploded! After a long lecture about keeping our surroundings clean, I was grounded for two weeks. That was definitely not a good way to start a vacation.

Being a litter bug is a bad thing because you disappoint your parents, but I also learned that I need to take care of the Earth.

By: Reese Icenogle

respect

rigor

responsibility

respect

rigor

responsibility

respect

rigor

Responsibility

My MP3 player was gone, in just a little more than a second! That's what happened when I did not step up and show responsibility!

Responsibility is not only doing things without being asked, but it's also about taking care of what is yours. You never want to learn responsibility the way I did! My way was tough, and believe me, you do not want to experience it!

One afternoon, I was playing in my room when my mom came in and said to come downstairs and pick up my MP3 player. I said, "Just a minute," and she left.

Thirty minutes later, my mom came in again and said to come down RIGHT NOW! "Okay, just one second," I said, buy Mom refused to listen.

She was so angry, she demanded, "No! Come down right now!" She threatened that I would lose my MP3 player if I did not pick it up NOW!

So, I went downstairs and picked it up, but I felt bad that I was not showing responsibility. I started crying because I felt so horrible. I apologized to my mom, and said that I would show responsibility next time and not ignore her. I not only got a bad feeling about how I hurt my mom's feelings, but I lost my MP3 player too.

So, that is how I learned the hard way about taking care of what is mine and showing responsibility.

By: Valerie Ulsh

Responsibility

"Camden, get down here right now! When are you going to learn to take responsibility for your school work?"

Mom was screaming at the top of her lungs, so I ran downstairs and saw her angrily holding my cursive package. It was work I had done my best to put off, but my mom found it in my backpack the last night of winter vacation. Busted!

Okay, so maybe I had plenty of time over break to practice my cursive. It's just that my vacation was filled with super, exciting, fun stuff, and the last thing I wanted to think of was "it!"

Mom told me I was grounded, and I would have to work on my handwriting every night for two weeks. I really got super angry at her, although I knew she was right, and I wasn't taking responsibility for my work. I still don't think she should have yelled so much, but okay, she had a point. I have to be responsible for all of my school work, not just the subjects I like. I need to concentrate on my study skills now, so I will do well in middle school and high school.

Being a responsible student is especially difficult when there are so many fun-packed days just waiting for me to participate. Responsibility means to find time for fun after you've finished your school work.

By: Camden Brown

respect

rigor

responsibility

respect

rigor

responsibility

respect

rigor

Responsibility

Hey! If you think responsibility isn't extremely important, you are sadly mistaken! Responsibility makes you a good person, and it's essential in your life. It is doing your best and taking care of things. Responsibility is also getting things done. It is knowing what you're supposed to do, even when nobody asks.

I'll never forget that day when I learned to take responsibility of my homework. I had just gotten back from soccer practice when my mom asked me, "Have you got all of your work done?"

"Oh no," I screamed. I had forgotten to do my homework! In a stern voice, my mom told me to sit down right away. I immediately organized my assignments and worked all night to get my homework done. Finally, I was finished and plopped into my bed, exhausted!

This is a little bit about why being a responsible person is such a necessity. One reason is to show others that you're a hard worker. Another reason is to be a good role model. I hope you now feel the same way about responsibility as I do.

By: Cole Henningsen

Responsibility

Talk about responsibility! Caring for ten pets takes a lot of time and energy, not to mention patience! If you don't like the smell of wet dog, then this is not the job for you!

When three dogs are running through the house, get out of the way! I live in a very crazy household filled with dogs, sugar gliders, snakes, birds and fish. The dogs try to eat the sugar gliders and the birds, but they're smart enough to stay away from the snakes.

My brother and I are responsible for taking care of the menagerie, and it's not as fun as it sounds. Each animal needs something different, and except for the fish, they all want attention at the same time. The sugar gliders bite if you don't constantly hold them, and the dogs are always into something. Feeding all of the animals is the easiest part of the job. You guessed it, the worst thing is cleaning up after three dogs.

I wouldn't give up any of our pets, but seriously, ten pets are a lot of work!

By: Ryan Egan

Rigor

I often stop and consider how I can show rigor. I'm still learning about it, but I know it's trying new things and striving to do my best.

When I got to the bus on the first day of school, my friend and I had different opinions about school. My friend was eager to learn and I was not. When we got to school, the day went by so slowly for both of us. The day dragged on because I was not eager to be there and my friend was full of enthusiasm.

When the time came for science class, I knew I needed to show rigor. I was afraid I wouldn't do well and I anticipated the worst. Then someone came around passing out papers. I looked at it and it made sense, so I immediately got to work. After I had finished, I glanced across the room and noticed my friend was stuck on a problem. Since I was done, I went over to see if he needed help. I explained it to him, and reassured him that he was doing a good job. When he finished he said, "Thank you for helping me with the problems!"

At the end of the lesson, I realized two things. First of all, science was fun, and second, I had done a good job in showing rigor!

By: Reilly Lavelle

respect

rigor

responsibility

respect

rigor

responsibility

respect

rigor

Rigor

When the pressure and the spotlight is on, you don't ever give up! A lot of disappointing things can happen when you don't show rigor. I am still learning a bit about rigor, but I know it means striving for excellence and always trying to do your best.

One day at school, we were preparing for tryouts for the spelling bee. I didn't get that much sleep the night before, so I was exhausted. I anxiously wrote the words on the paper as my teacher called them out, not really concentrating on what I was doing. Some of the words were difficult, so I was just guessing on many of them, hurrying to get it over with. Eventually the test was over, and we graded them at once. I ended up missing two words, and realized I was not showing a lot of rigor. I watched in disappointment and jealousy when the kids that succeeded stepped up and won the chance to compete in the spelling bee. What a bummer!

The day when the final spelling bee was going on, I watched excitedly until both of my classmates missed their words and were eliminated from the competition. I learned that rigor does not come easily, but if you try really hard, you will succeed!

By: Dylan George

respect

rigor

responsibility

respect

rigor

responsibility

respect

rigor

Rigor

Guess what? Just as I was going to give up on myself, I learned how lucky I am to have rigor!

Has someone ever told you not to give up and you can do it? That's what happened to me. One evening, I was playing baseball and it was already 9:00. I was so tired, I couldn't hit the ball. I just wanted to stop playing when my sister said, "You can do it! Don't give up!" That was all I needed to try my hardest, and I hit a home run! I was so excited, and I couldn't believe it. Then my sister said, "I knew you could do it."

That was the night I learned how lucky I was to have rigor. My sister used rigor to encourage me, and I used it to strive to do my very best. I will always use rigor when I am going to give up! It really helped me handle a difficult situation and come out on top.

By: Gianna Biggerstaff

respect   responsibility   rigor   respect   responsibility   rigor

respect

rigor

responsibility

respect

rigor

responsibility

respect

Rigor

Do you know what it feels like when you want something really bad and you have to work extremely hard to earn it? Demonstrating rigor is a ton of work! I'm sure you realize that some of the ways to show rigor are working hard, trying your best, being a good role model and such. But have you ever had to actually show rigor? I have!

I want to be a babysitter some day, but I'll have to prove to Mom and Dad that I'm responsible enough for the job. In order to take care of small children, you must know how to react quickly in all kinds of situations.

One time, I had to be a good role model for my younger siblings. My mom had just left the house and my dad was out of sight when my brother started throwing hard toys, so I asked him to stop. Then my other brother whined because he wanted something to play with, and my little sister started acting silly and stole my important pen-pal letter. Boy, did I get worked up! "Hey," I screamed. Then I thought about how much I wanted to be a babysitter. I calmly retrieved my paper, and found a toy for my little brother to play with. When Dad came back, I was proud of myself because I had shown rigor by doing my best and being a patient role model during a difficult time.

I hope now I will be more confident. Who knows? Maybe someday I'll be a babysitter. No, I'm positive I will be a babysitter, and I'll do a terrific job, always remembering how important it is to show rigor.

By: Kyra Mowry

respect

responsibility

rigor

respect

responsibility

rigor

respect

responsibility

respect

rigor

responsibility

respect

rigor

responsibility

respect

rigor

Rigor

Have you ever been really enthusiastic about showing rigor? I've used it many times, and I'm always looking for more possibilities.

One afternoon, I was able to show rigor when I was available to help a neighbor. She wanted to learn how to ride a two-wheeler, so I loaned her a little blue bike. I patiently worked with her, and taught her how to ride it. The first time she tried, she expected to be really good, but she leaned to one side and tumbled. I told her not to give up and explained that no one ever gets it the first time. I continued to encourage her and reminded her to try hard and do her very best. Every morning, I helped her until she became really good and was able to ride on her own.

My neighbor was so proud of herself, and I felt sure that rigor would be contagious. I knew that because I showed rigor by being a good role model, she would end up doing the same by helping someone else.

By: Samantha Bryson

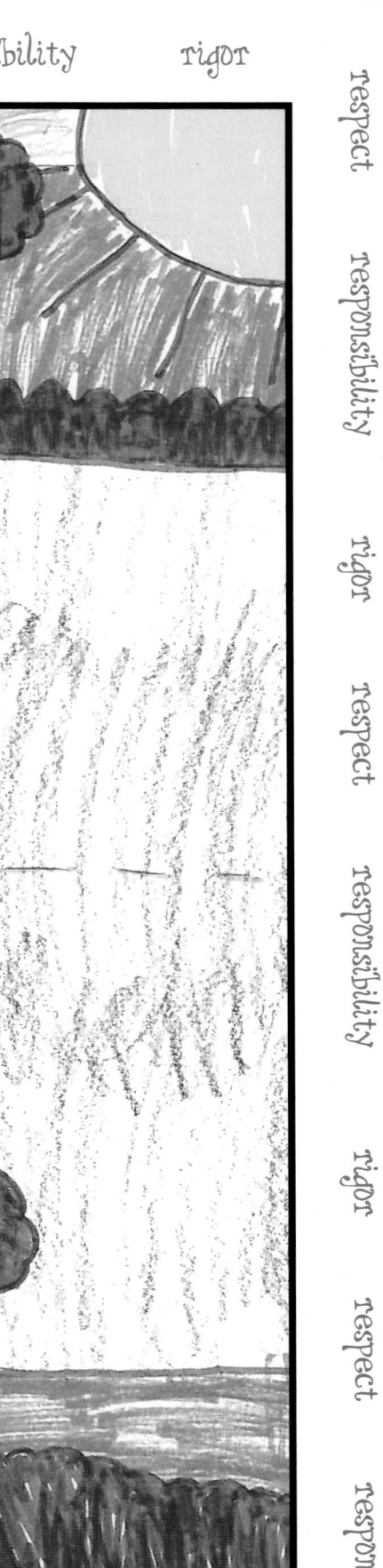

respect

rigor

responsibility

respect

rigor

responsibility

respect

rigor

Rigor

Do you ever think about how you can show rigor? I probably wouldn't put a lot of thought into it either, but I'm interested because we are studying it in school. One way to show rigor is to work hard, always trying to do your best. I continually try to use rigor in school because I have to work hard to do well.

One sunny morning, I couldn't wait to get to school. Science class was going to be extra special because we were going to learn about the water cycle. Science is my favorite subject, especially when we are learning about something new and exciting. But once we got started, I was so frustrated because it was the hardest thing I had ever learned. I said to myself, "I have been stuck on this problem for ten minutes! What now?" Then it came to me...Rigor! I had to use rigor to try harder and really concentrate on the problem. I just couldn't give up! Finally, I understood how it worked, and I also realized I could accomplish anything when I just calmed down and used rigor.

I learned that I should always remember to use rigor when life gets a little rough. I also realized that I could ask others for help like I did when I was stuck on the science problem. Rigor not only means working your hardest, but also knowing when to get help so you can succeed.

By: Evan Smith

respect   responsibility   rigor

CR3	Assembly	Playground	Cafeteria	Hallways	Entering/ Exiting	Bus/ Bus Stop	Bathroom	Library	Computer Lab
RESPECT Self Others Property	-Listen to presenters	-Listen to adults -Use kind words and actions towards others -Resolve conflicts peacefully -Display good sportsmanship by playing fair	-Listen to adults -Respect property by cleaning tables and floors -Say "Please and thank you"	-Keep hands off displays -Respect personal space	-Follow adult directions	-Bikes yield to pedestrians -Keep hands to self and respect space	-Keep bathrooms clean -Respect privacy -Be considerate of self, others and property	-Listen to adults -Be considerate of others working -Take care of library books -Share center materials	-Follow adult directions -Keeps hands off of other student's computer -Respect personal space
RESPONSIBILITY What are you expected to do?	-Keep hands and feet to self -Sit flat -Clap when appropriate -Enter and exit quietly and calmly	-Know and follow rules -Line up when whistle blows -Put all balls and playground equipment away when the bell rings -Play safely	-Clean up after yourself -Make healthy food choices -Stay seated until dismissed -Follow good table manners	-Use Coyote signal to quiet others in hallway -Stay to the right when walking -Use walking feet	-Arrive to school between 7:35-7:40am -Use crosswalks -Use walking feet -Enter and exit school calmly and quietly	-Sit while on the bus -Know and follow bus rules -Respect public property at bus stop	-Flush every time -Wash hands -Enter and exit quietly -Return bathroom pass when finished	-Return books on time -Use shelf marker -Follow directions -Clean center when finished -Stamp date and due slip -Use time wisely	-Keep your hands and feet to yourself -Use your own hands on your own keyboard -Help by telling or showing not doing
RIGOR Strive for excellence Accomplish goals Do your best Set a good example	-Listen with the intent to learn	-Include others -Be a good example and role model for others -Demonstrate leadership	-Welcome others to your table	-Notice displays so you learn from other's work	-Arrive to school on time and ready to learn	-Arrive to the bus stop on time -Go directly to the bus after school -Follow bus rules consistently	-Use time wisely	-Read silently after choosing a book -Study -Research -Participate in centers	-Use time wisely -Try to solve your own problems
Voice levels	0-2	0-4	0-2	0-1	0-1	0-2	0-1	0-1	0-1

Voice Levels: 0=No voice   1=whisper   2=inside voice   3=outside voice   4=emergency voice